Liz and Joe
Have a Day Out

Liz and Joe Series

by Jennie Cole

Gate
HOUSE

Liz and Joe Have a Day Out
Copyright © Jennie Cole 2014

Published in 2014 by Gatehouse Media Limited

ISBN: 978-1-84231-103-5

British Library Cataloguing-in-Publication Data:
A catalogue record for this book is available from the British Library

Author's Note

I am an ESOL tutor based in Leeds. I was inspired by the Gatehouse Books I used with my students to write some beginner reading material of my own, using my own photographs and text. I designed them in comic book style, to appeal to a wider audience, and aimed the text at the Entry level 1 and 2 ESOL learner.

The *Liz and Joe* series is very popular with my students, who enjoy following the same characters, seeing different aspects of their lives and comparing everyday situations with their own.

It is exciting and rewarding to have them published by Gatehouse Books.

Jennie Cole

5

Liz and Joe saw lots of signs.

They crossed a bridge...

...and saw some water.

The water was from a waterfall.

Liz and Joe saw the hat.

Liz was so happy.

I'm so happy I found my hat!

Liz and Joe celebrated and ate some lunch.

13

They walked back to the car.

Liz and Joe were ready to go home.

It's been a great day, Liz.

Yes, a real adventure, Joe!

Get Talking!

Have you ever lost something?

How did you feel?

What happened?

Gatehouse Books®

Gatehouse Books are written for older teenagers and adults who are developing their basic reading and writing or English language skills.

The format of our books is clear and uncluttered. The language is familiar and the text is often line-broken, so that each line ends at a natural pause.

Gatehouse Books are widely used within Adult Basic Education throughout the English speaking world. They are also a valuable resource within the Prison Education Service and Probation Services, Social Services and secondary schools - both in basic skills and ESOL teaching.

Catalogue available

Gatehouse Media Limited
PO Box 965
Warrington
WA4 9DE

Tel: 01925 267778
E-mail: info@gatehousebooks.com
Website: www.gatehousebooks.com